② performed 4/26/09
w/ U of M LIFE
SCIENCES DEPT @
HILL AUD,

CHORAL FINALE
TO THE
NINTH SYMPHONY

*For Chorus of Mixed Voices,
Soli and Orchestra*

By

LUDWIG VAN BEETHOVEN
Op. 125

On Schiller's "Ode To Joy"

English Version by
HENRY G. CHAPMAN

Ed. 789

NAN WASHBURN, PSO

G. SCHIRMER, Inc.
DISTRIBUTED BY
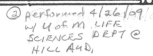
HAL•LEONARD®
CORPORATION
7777 W. BLUEMOUND RD. P.O. BOX 13819 MILWAUKEE, WI 53213

TO JOY

JOY, thou spark from flame immortal,
    Daughter of Elysium!
Drunk with fire, O heav'n-born Goddess,
    We invade thy halidom!
Let thy magic bring together
    All whom earth-born laws divide;
All mankind shall be as brothers
    'Neath thy tender wings and wide.

He that's had that best good fortune,
    To his friend a friend to be,
He that's won a noble woman,
    Let him join our Jubilee!
Ay, and who a single other
    Soul on earth can call his own;
But let him who ne'er achieved it
    Steal away in tears alone.

Joy doth every living creature
    Draw from Nature's ample breast,
All the good and all the evil
    Follow on her roseate quest.
Kisses doth she give, and vintage,
    Friends who firm in death have stood,
Joy of life the worm receiveth,
    And the Angels dwell with God!

Glad as burning suns that glorious
    Through the heavenly spaces sway,
    Haste ye, brothers, on your way,
Joyous as a knight victorious.

Love toward countless millions swelling,
    Wafts one kiss to all the world!
    Surely, o'er yon stars unfurl'd,
Some kind Father has his dwelling!

Fall ye prostrate, O ye millions?
    Dost thy Maker feel, O world?
    Seek Him o'er yon stars unfurl'd,
O'er the stars rise His pavilions!

From the German of Schiller
by HENRY G. CHAPMAN

21838

Choral Finale
to the
Ninth Symphony
on
Schiller's "Ode to Joy"

English version by
Henry G. Chapman

Ludwig van Beethoven. Op.125

Copyright, 1910, by G. Schirmer, Inc.
Copyright renewed, 1938, by G. Schirmer, Inc.

Printed in the U.S.A.

4

O Broth - - - ers, no more such mu-sic!
O Freun - - - de, nicht die - se Tö - ne!

Ra - ther let us now_____
son - dern lasst uns an - -

_____ our voic-es raise in__ sweet-er, more joy - -
- ge - neh-me-re an - stim-men, und freu - -

laws di - vide, All ___ man-kind shall be as broth-ers 'Neath thy ten - der
streng ge - teilt; al - le Men-schen wer-den Brü - der, wo dein sanf-ter

laws di - vide, All ___ man-kind shall be as broth-ers 'Neath thy ten - der
streng ge - teilt; al - le Men-schen wer-den Brü - der, wo dein sanf-ter

laws di - vide, All ___ man-kind shall be as broth-ers 'Neath thy ten - der
streng ge - teilt; al - le Men-schen wer-den Brü - der, wo dein sanf-ter

wings and wide.
Flü - gel weilt.

wings and wide.
Flü - gel weilt.

wings and wide.
Flü - gel weilt.

p dolce

Allegro assai vivace alla marcia (♩.=84)

Tenor Solo

Glad,   glad   as burn-ing suns, as burn-ing
Froh,   froh,   wie sei - ne Son - nen, sei - ne

pp

suns that glo - rious, Glad as burn - ing suns that_ glo - rious
Son - nen flie - gen,_ froh wie sei - ne Son - nen_ flie - gen_

poco cresc.

Thro' the heav'n-ly spac - es_ sway,   Haste, ye broth-ers,_
durch des Him - mels prächt'- gen_ Plan,   lau - fet Brü - der,_

on your way,   haste, ye broth-ers,_ on_ your
eu - re Bahn   lau - fet, Brü - der_ eu - re_

We in - vade thy hal - i - dom! Let thy
Himm - li - sche, dein Hei - lig - tum! Dei - ne

We in - vade thy hal - i - dom! Let thy
Himm - li - sche, dein Hei - lig - tum! Dei - ne

We in - vade thy hal - i - dom! Let thy
Himm - li - sche, dein Hei - lig - tum! Dei - ne

We in - vade thy hal - i - dom! Let thy
Himm - li - sche, dein Hei - lig - tum! Dei - ne

ma - gic bring to - geth - er All whom earth - born
Zau - ber bin - den wie - der, was die Mo - de

ma - gic bring to - geth - er All whom earth - born
Zau - ber bin - den wie - der, was die Mo - de

ma - gic bring to - geth - er All whom earth - born
Zau - ber bin - den wie - der, was die Mo - de

ma - gic bring to - geth - er All whom earth - born
Zau - ber bin - den wie - der, was die Mo - de

595

all the world, to all the world! ___
gan - zen Welt, der all gan - zen Welt! ___

all, to all the world! _
gan - zen, gan - zen Welt! _

all the world, to
gan - zen Welt, der

We in - vade thy hal - - i - dom! ___
Himm - li - sche, dein Hei - - lig - tum! ___

Joy, thou spark from flame im - mor - tal, Daugh-ter of E -
Freu - de, schö - ner Göt - ter-fun - ken, Toch-ter aus E -

all the world! _____ Love ___ toward
gan - zen Welt! _____ Seid ___ um -

Love! ___ toward count - less mil - lions
Seid ___ um - schlun - gen, Mil - li -

non legato

be articulate in diction thru here. Just touch each word.

bring to - geth - er__ All whom earth-born laws _____ di - vide;
bin - den __ wie - der __ was die Mo - de streng _____ ge - teilt.

bring to - geth - er All whom earth-born laws _____ di - vide;
bin - den wie - der was die Mo - de streng _____ ge - teilt.

bring to - geth - er__ All whom earth-born laws _____ di - vide;
bin - den wie - der__ was die Mo - de streng _____ ge - teilt.

bring to - geth - er All whom earth-born laws _____ di - vide;
bin - den wie - der was die Mo - de streng _____ ge - teilt.

look up

All __ man - kind, __ all man -
Al - le Men-schen, al - le

All __ man - kind, __ all man -
Al - le Men-schen, al - le

All __ man - kind, __ all man -
Al - le Men-schen, al - le

All __ man - kind, __ all man -
Al - le Men-schen, al - le

21838

Prestissimo